WIRE EDM ESSENTIALS: 1ST Edition

Philip Roberts

10/11/19

P.R. Publishing Company LLC

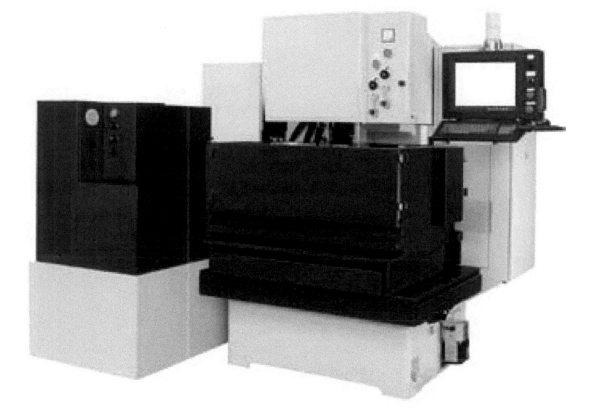

2019, Philip Roberts

Table of Contents

CHAPTER 1
INTRODUCTION
TO
EDM

ELECTRICAL DISCHARGE MACHINING

Chapter 1: Basic Introduction to EDM

What is EDM?

EDM (Electrical Discharge Machining) is a thermal erosion process, in that it uses the heat generated from a spark to melt away the work material.

What can be EDM machined?

Any material that is electrically conductive (able to conduct electricity), can be EDM machined. The hardness of the material does not matter.

What are the three main types of EDM?

EDM Sinker (Also known as: Ram, Conventional, and Vertical EDM)

A) The result of the cavity machined, is a reverse image of the shape of the tool used.
B) The shape can be machined partially through the workpiece, or completely through the workpiece.

Wire EDM (Also known as: Traveling wire EDM)

A) The result of the cavity machined is of a 2D programmed path.
B) The shape machined must be completely through the workpiece.

EDM Drill (Also known as: Fast hole, and Small Precision Hole EDM)

A) The result of the cavity machined, is a reverse image of the shape of the tool used.
B) The shape can be machined partially through the workpiece, or completely through the workpiece.

What is an electrode?

An electrode is used to conduct the electricity by way of a spark to that work piece.

A) For an EDM Sinker machine the electrode material is normally either Graphite, Copper, Copper Graphite, Tungsten, or Copper Tungsten.

B) For a Wire EDM machine the electrode material is normally either Soft Brass wire, Half Hard Brass wire, Molly wire, Stratified wire, or Zinc coated Brass wire.

C) For an EDM Drill machine the electrode material is normally either Brass tubing, or Copper tubing.

What is Dielectric Fluid?

Dielectric fluid is a dielectric material in a liquid state. Dielectric liquids are used as electrical insulators in high voltage applications, e.g. transformers, capacitors, high voltage cables, and switchgear (namely high voltage switchgear). Its main purpose is to prevent or rapidly quench electric discharges. In EDM the temperature and the conductivity of the dielectric fluid is commonly controlled. Its main purpose is to prevent fires, and to flush away the vaporized material.

A) In an EDM Sinker machine the dielectric fluid is a special EDM Oil.

B) In Wire EDM machines the dielectric fluid is De-Ionized Water.

C) In an EDM Drill machine the dielectric fluid is normally De-Ionized Water. (In some cases EDM Oil is used.)

What is EDM used for and/or why use EDM for machining?

A) Hard material and/or material that is too hard to machine. As in Rockwell hardness.

B) Material that needs to stay burr free. There is no force in EDM because the electrode does not come into contact with the work material.

C) Things that are too difficult to machine conventionally. (Ribs, small shapes, small holes, sharp corners)

What are <u>some</u> industries that use EDM, and what for?

A) Tool and Die. (Stamping Dies, Punches and Dies, Progressive Dies)

B) Mold Making. (Plastic Injection Molds, Blow Molds, Vacuum Molds)

C) Automotive. (Fuel Injectors)

D) Aerospace. (Seal Slots, Vent Holes, Cooling Holes)

E) Land Based Turbines. (Same as Aerospace components)

F) Medical. (Bone Screws, Spine Inserts)

G) Knife Manufactures. (Sharp Edges, Engraving Designs.)

H) Jewelry Manufactures. (Shapes)

I) Gun Manufactures. (Barrel Porting)

J) Cutting tools. (Flush Holes, Form Tools)

K) Extrusion Die Company's

L) Electronic Component Company's. (Small Connectors)

What are the main components of an EDM machine?

A) Power Supply (For generating a D.C. Current at set frequencies.)

B) Dielectric System (Introduce dielectric into the cut to wash away the debris, cool the electrode and part, and to filter the dielectric debris.)

C) Electrode (For delivering the electric spark to the workpiece.)

D) Servo System (To control infeed of the electrode into the part.)

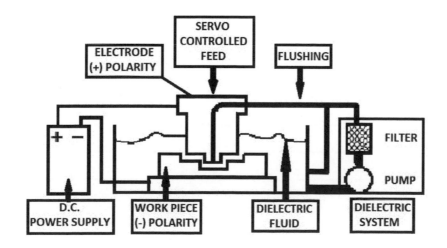

NOTES:

CHAPTER 2

THE

EDM

PROCESS

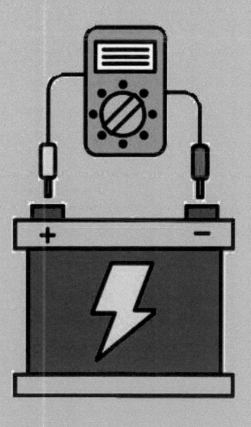

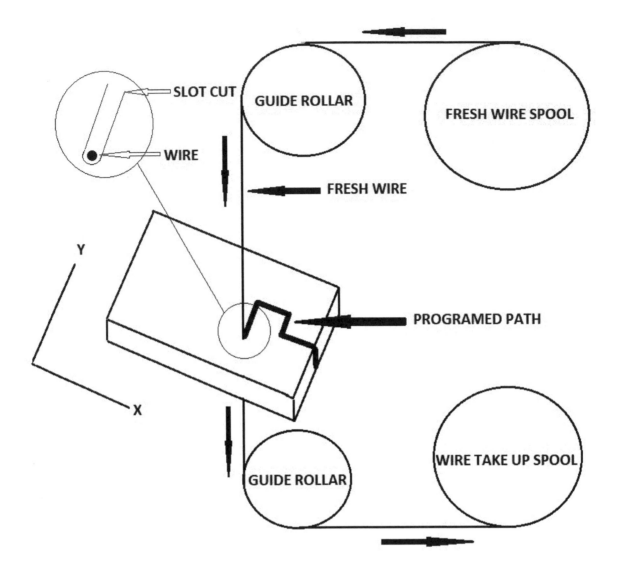

HOW DOES IT WORK

Chapter 2: The EDM Process

How does it work?

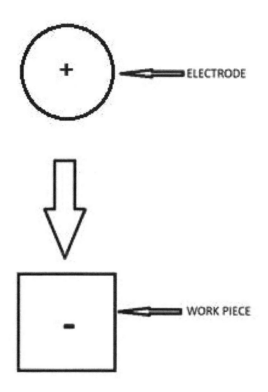

FIG 1

FIG 1

A (D.C.) electrical charge is applied to the electrode and the work piece.

The electrode is advanced through the dielectric fluid towards the workpiece.

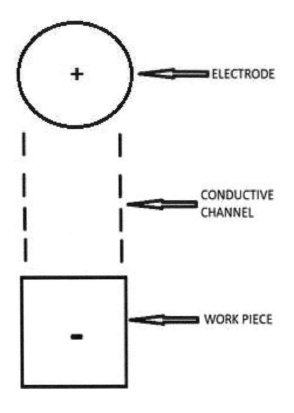

FIG 2

FIG 2

As the electrode advances closer to the work piece, a conductive channel forms between the electrode and the workpiece.

This happens because of the electrical potential difference between the electrode and the workpiece, and because of the breakdown of the insulating restraints of the dielectric fluid, due to the voltage that is applied.

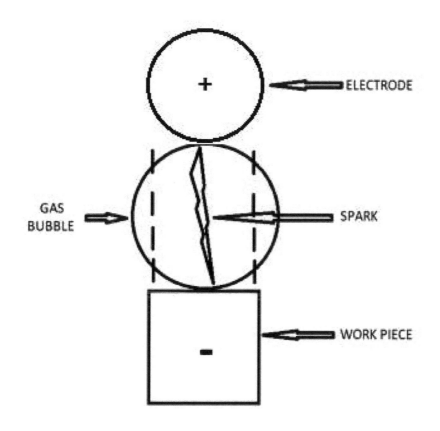

FIG 3

FIG 3

Eventually the electrode gets close enough to the work piece where a spark can jump the gap.

As soon as the spark occurs, a gas bubble forms around it.

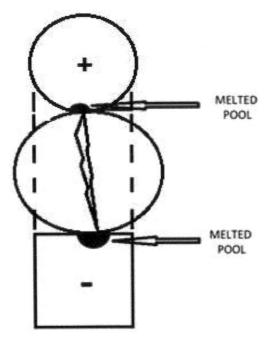

MELTED
POOL

MELTED
POOL

FIG 4

FIG 4

The heat that is generated by the spark, begins melting a pool of material at both ends of the spark.

The size of the pool is determined by:
   a) The amount of amperage supplied to the spark. (PEAK CURRENT)
   b) The melting point of the material.
   c) How long the spark is turned on. (ON TIME)

Note: There is only one spark generated at a time from the generator.

Note: It appears to the human eye that many sparks are being generated at one time, because the human eye cannot react as fast as the speed that the sparks are being turned on and off.

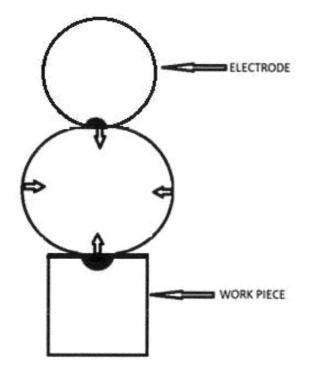

ELECTRODE

WORK PIECE

FIG 5

FIG 5

The (D.C.) electrical charge is removed from the electrode and the work piece.

The spark stops.

The conductive channel dissipates.

No more gasses are being produced, therefore the bubble Implodes.

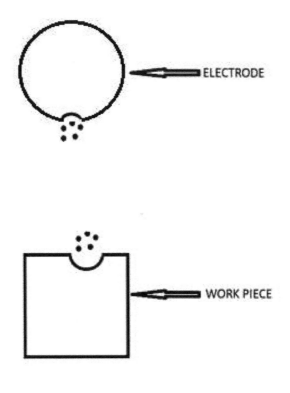

FIG 6

FIG 6

The pressure from the implosion of the gas bubble, pops the molten material from melted pools, out into the open, where it cools and solidifies back to solid particles.

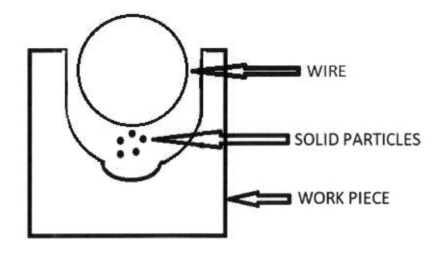

WIRE

SOLID PARTICLES

WORK PIECE

FIG 7

FIG 7

The solid particles are now trapped between the electrode and the work piece, and need to be completely evacuated from the cut.

If the solid particles (debris) is not evacuated from the cut, unstable EDM cutting conditions can occur, or short circuiting can occur. (This can lead to a D.C. Arc)

Therefore a delay is made, before the next spark is generated, allowing time to flush the solid particles out of the cut. (OFF TIME)

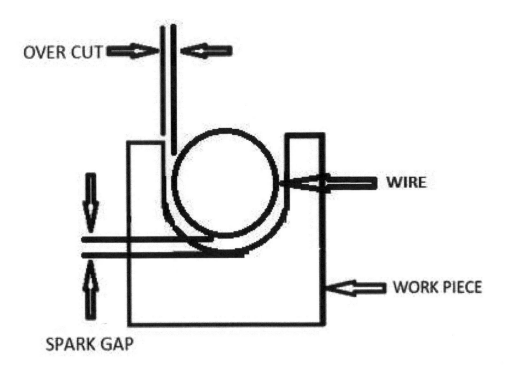

SPARK GAP

SPARK GAP is the distance between the **ELECTRODE** and the **WORKPIECE** during the EDM process.

OVER CUT

OVER CUT is the distance between the **ELECTRODE** and the **WORKPIECE** after the EDM process is complete.

NOTES:

The three main settings in EDM

The three main setting in EDM are **ON TIME, OFF TIME,** and **PEAK CURRENT.**

ON TIME is the length of time that each individual spark is turned on for. This value is measured in microseconds. (1 microsecond is equal to 1/1,000,000 of a second.)

OFF TIME is the amount of time between the individual sparks. This is the amount of time that is set for flushing the solid particles (Debris) from the cut. This value is measured in microseconds. (1 microsecond is equal to 1/1,000,000 of a second.)

PEAK CURRENT is the amount of current that is made available to each spark. This value is measured in amps.

The three main results (concerns) in EDM

The three main results or concerns in EDM are **SPEED, WEAR,** and **FINISH.**

SPEED is the metal removal rate of the cut. This value is expressed in Cubic Inches per Hour.

WEAR is the percentage of wear that occurs on the electrode during the cut. This value is expressed in Percentage. (Wear is not a concern in wire EDM because the wire is constantly being replenished from a spool of wire.)

FINISH is the average surface finish roughness that is developed during the cut. This value is expressed in Micro Inches. (European value is expressed in VDI, and Asian value is expressed in CH, or Micro Meters)

The effects of three main settings, and additional settings

ON TIME
Speed, Wear, Finish, and Overcut.

OFF TIME
Flushing time and Stability.

PEAK CURRENT
Speed (In conjunction with On Time), Finish, and Overcut.

HIGH VOLTAGE
Stability.

SERVO
Infeed speed adjustment.

GAP
Voltage adjustment for the distance between the electrode and the work piece.

Metal removal rate, and surface finish

PEAK CURRENT

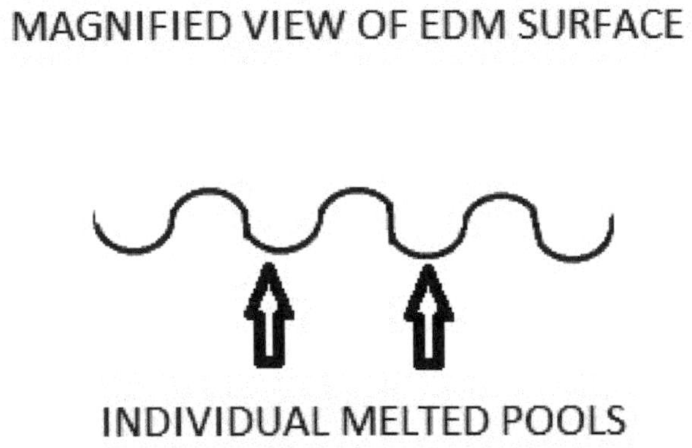

MAGNIFIED VIEW OF EDM SURFACE

INDIVIDUAL MELTED POOLS

FIG 8

FIG 8

As stated earlier in this book, the heat from each spark melts a pool of material, on the surface of the work piece.

If the surface is magnified, the surface looks like a mountain range. (With each valley being a result of the melted pool.)

The amount of **PEAK CURRENT** used determines how far the sparks heat can penetrate into the workpiece, or how large of a pool of melted material can be obtained. (Provided the proper amount of **ON TIME** is used in conjunction with the **PEAK CURRENT**.)

Therefore, the more peak current that is used, the faster the **Metal Removal Rate** becomes, the larger the pool of melted material becomes, and the rougher the **surface finish** gets.

ON TIME

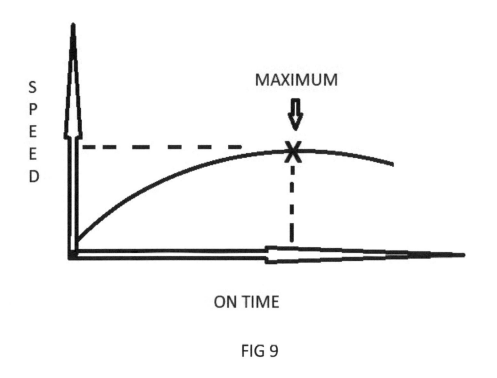

FIG 9

FIG 9

If there is no **ON TIME**, there is no spark.

As the **ON TIME** of the spark is increased, the size of the melted pool of material increases, and the **METAL REMOVAL RATE** (SPEED) increases.

Eventually the spark has been turned on long enough to the point that it has generated the most heat that it can generate, has penetrated as far into the part it can penetrate, and has melted the largest pool of material that it can melt. (The point marked maximum in fig 9.)

If the **ON TIME** of the spark is increased more, the **METAL REMOVAL RATE** (SPEED) decreases.

At this maximum efficient point of ON TIME, the spark has done the most efferent amount of work that it can.

FIG 10

FIG 10

If the **ON TIME** is set to the maximum efficient amount of **ON TIME**, the largest pool of melted material is created for that specific spark.

If the **ON TIME** is set to a shorter time, the size of the melted pool is smaller.

It is critical to have the correct **ON TIME** for maximum **METAL REMOVAL RATE**.

However a shorter **ON TIME** can be used to create a smaller pool, to achieve a smoother **surface finish**.

VARIABLES:

The maximum ON TIME value changes for different electrode materials.

The maximum ON TIME value changes for different work materials.

The maximum ON TIME value changes for different amounts of PEAK CURRENT.

OFF TIME AND DUTY CYCLE:

ON TIME
(ON TIME + OFF TIME) = DUTY CYCLE

Another way to increase **Metal Removal Rate**, is to make sure that the best possible duty cycle is used.

To do this the operator must lock in the maximum efficient amount of **ON TIME**, and then decrease the **OFF TIME** as much as possible without creating instability, or dangerous cutting conditions. For example **ON TIME** = 100, **OFF TIME** = 75 or 25.

100 / (100 + 75) = .57 x 100 = **57 % Efficiency**

100 / (100 + 25) = .80 x 100 = **80 % Efficiency**

To better understand how a more efficient **DUTY CYCLE** helps with **Metal Removal Rate,** let's look at it one individual cycle.

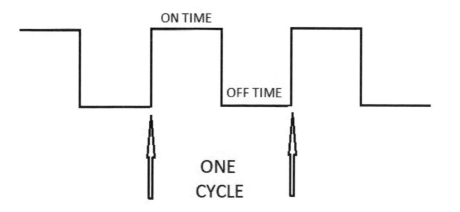

One complete cycle is one sparks **ON TIME** plus one sparks **OFF TIME**.

So how much of that cycle actually has material being removed (Spark On), determines how efficient the cycle is.

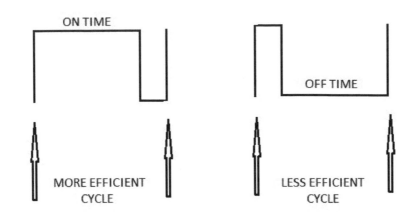

NOTES: _____

_____

_____

_____

_____

_____

_____

_____

_____

_____

_____

_____

_____

_____

_____

_____

_____

_____

_____

_____

CHAPTER 3 DEFINING LOCATIONS

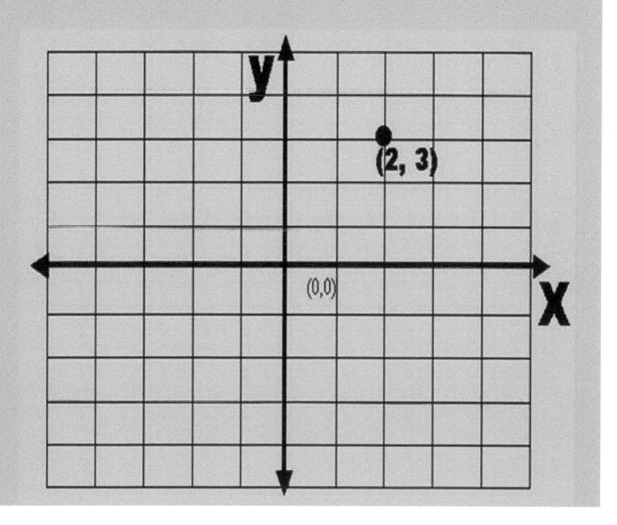

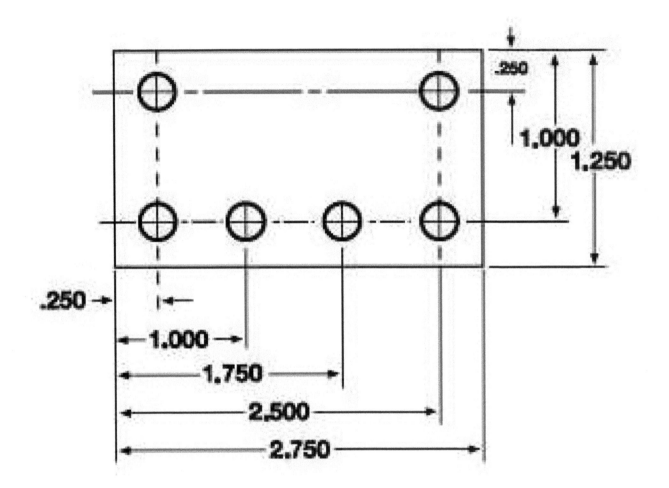

Chapter3: Defining Locations

The Cartesian coordinate system

CNC machines position using the Cartesian Coordinate System. The Cartesian Coordinate System contains a horizontal X-axis, and a vertical Y-axis.

At the point where X and Y intersect is called the origin. The origins coordinates are labeled (X0 Y0), commonly referred to as "Part Zero".

This "Part Zero" origin is defined by the operator. Then the operator programs locations (Or moves) based on the "Part Zero", using the Cartesian Coordinate System.

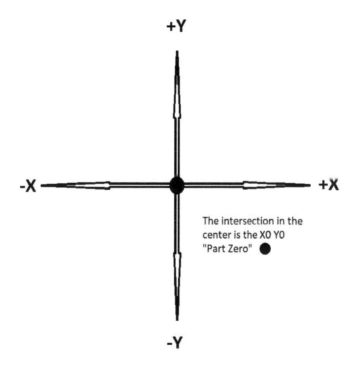

Many machines work internally to an internal origin that is defined as "Machine Home". However these internal working calculations are irrelevant to the operator, except when a problem occurs.

Plotting the points (Locations, or moves) using the Cartesian Coordinate System.

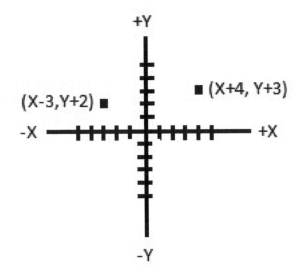

When plotting the points coordinates, using the Cartesian Coordinate System, the graph has "tick marks" along the X, and Y axis.

These "tick marks" denote the scale that is being used. For example 1 tick mark may equal 1 inch.

First you count along the X axis until you find the tick mark representing your X axis coordinate, then you count along the Y axis until you find the tick mark representing your Y axis coordinate. The intersection point is the location of your coordinate point.

Note that, in this example the X0 Y0 origin has always stayed at the center intersection of the X and Y axis.

Absolute and Incremental Modes

Most machines have two modes of operation when it comes to interpreting the points plotted using the Cartesian coordinate system. Absolute (G90) and Incremental. (G91)

Up until now we have been using the example of Absolute Mode.

Absolute Mode (G90)

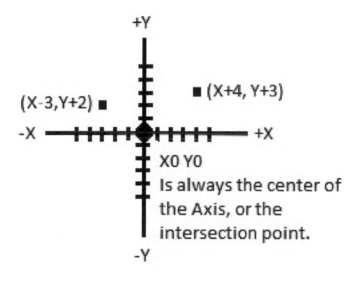

Absolute Mode is where a series of numerical positions are plotted in reference to a fixed X0 Y0 origin. (The center of the Cartesian Coordinate System)

The Absolute Mode is the most common way of programming, and the way we will program in our examples, given in this book.

Incremental Mode (G91)

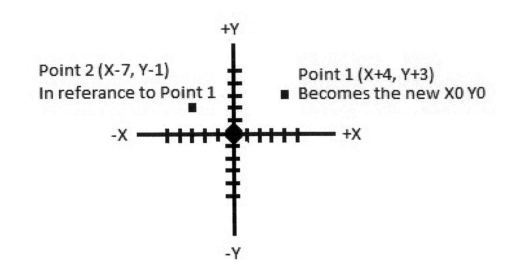

Incremental Mode is where a series of numerical positions are plotted in reference to each previous point location.

In other words the first point plotted is in reference to the center X0 Y0 origin (The center of the Cartesian Coordinate System), just like in Absolute Mode, But then the point plotted becomes the new X0 Y0 origin, and the next point plotted is in reference to that origin.

This continues for all the points plotted thereafter.

NOTES: _____

_____

_____

_____

_____

_____

_____

_____

_____

Absolute Exercise

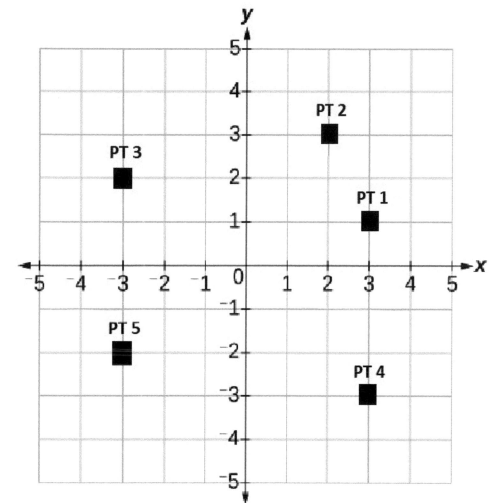

Define the move to Point 1   X= _____ Y= _____
Define the move to Point 2   X= _____ Y= _____
Define the move to Point 3   X= _____ Y= _____
Define the move to Point 4   X= _____ Y= _____
Define the move to Point 5   X= _____ Y= _____

Incremental Exercise

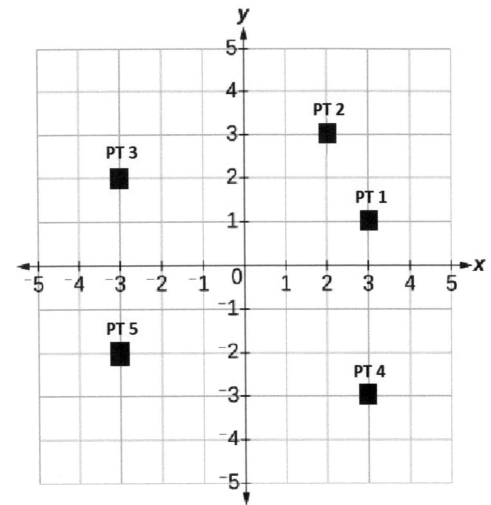

Define the move to Point 1   X= _____   Y=_____

Define the move to Point 2   X= _____   Y=_____

Define the move to Point 3   X= _____   Y=_____

Define the move to Point 4   X= _____   Y=_____

Define the move to Point 5   X= _____   Y=_____

Absolute Exercise Answers

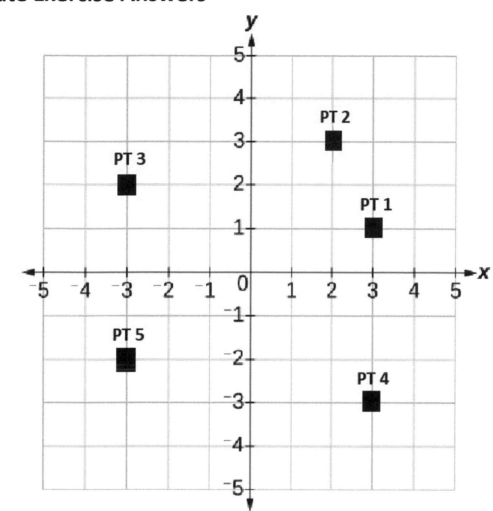

Define the move to Point 1	X= +3.0000	Y= +1.0000	
Define the move to Point 2	X= +2.0000	Y= +3.0000	
Define the move to Point 3	X= - 3.0000	Y= +2.0000	
Define the move to Point 4	X= +3.0000	Y= - 3.0000	
Define the move to Point 5	X= - 3.0000	Y= - 2.0000	

Incremental Exercise Answers

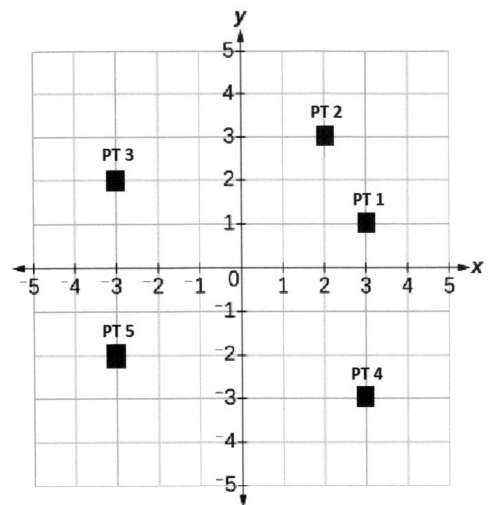

Define the move to Point 1   X= +3.0000   Y= +1.0000
Define the move to Point 2   X= - 1.0000   Y= +2.0000
Define the move to Point 3   X= - 5.0000   Y= - 1.0000
Define the move to Point 4   X= +6.0000   Y= - 5.0000
Define the move to Point 5   X= - 6.0000   Y= +1.0000

CHAPTER 4
GETTING THE MACHINE
READY FOR OPERATION

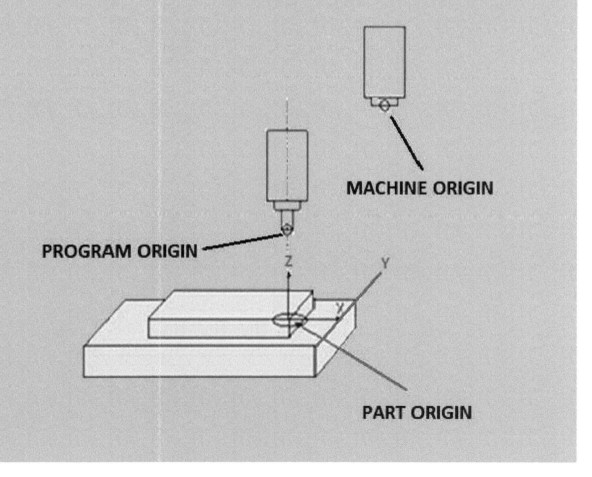

MACHINE ORIGIN

PROGRAM ORIGIN

PART ORIGIN

ABSOLUTE		RELATIVE		MACHINE	
X	0.0000	X	10.0000	X	285.7401
Y	5.0000	Y	0.0000	Y	39.2569
U	0.0000	U	0.0000	U	49.6005
V	0.0000	V	0.0000	V	50.2001
Z	146.6667	Z	146.6667	Z	146.6667
W	463.3933	W	463.3933	W	0.0000

WORK		START COOR		BREAK COOR	
X	41.1856	X	285.7401	X	285.7401
Y	-28.9356	Y	39.2569	Y	39.2569
U	0.7000	U	49.6005	U	49.6005
V	0.0000	V	50.2001	V	50.2001
Z	146.6667	Z	146.6667	Z	146.6667
W	1257.0423	W	0.0000	W	0.0000

Chapter 4: Getting the machine ready for operation

Starting the machine

Most CNC machines have a procedure that needs to be followed when first powered up. For example some may have a warm up period. Consult your manufacture for specific details.

Most CNC machines have a procedure for homing the machine when first powered up.

Homing the machine

Homing the machine is a procedure that lets the machine find and re-set its internal permanent origin. This procedure varies from machine to machine, but next is an example of how to start up and home the Wire EDM machine used for this Book.

NOTES: _____

_____

_____

_____

_____

_____

_____

_____

_____

Example for one machines start up and homing procedure (For a Wire EDM machine)

1. Turn Selector Switch to **ON**.

2. Pull & Turn (CW) **Emergency Stop**

3. Wait for software to finish booting up, then press the **Power** button.

4. If the wire is threaded, press the Wire Cut button on the hand pendent.

5. Click on the **MANUAL** function on the screen.

6. Press the **JOG** button, on the hand pendent, until the green light is on.

7. Select the **X100** feed rate, on the hand pendent, until the green light is on.

8. These are the buttons that will be used for Manual movement.

9. Move the Z axis up to a safe height above all obstructions.

10. Move –X until approximately 3 inches from the left rail.

11. Move –Y until approximately 3 inches from the front rail.

12. Click on the **Home Search** function, on the screen.

13. Click on the **Z Home** function, on the screen. (The Z axis should begin moving +Z) Wait for the beep.

14. Repeat steps 12, and 13 for X.

15. Repeat steps 12, and 13 for Y.

16. Repeat steps 12, and 13 for U.

17. Repeat steps 12, and 13 for V.

18. Press the **VERT** button, on the hand pendent. (Vertical Return)

19. Check for the green light on the VERT button, after all movement stops.

20. The machine is now homed, and the wire has been returned to square.

Setting the Z axis soft limit

The next thing we need to do, is to set the soft limit for Z so that we do not crash the upper head into anything.

1. Press the **JOG** button, on the hand pendent, until the green light is on.

2. Move the Z axis down to approximately .800 above the part.

3. Click on the soft limit function, on the screen, until it is updated, and red in color. (Red means soft limit active)

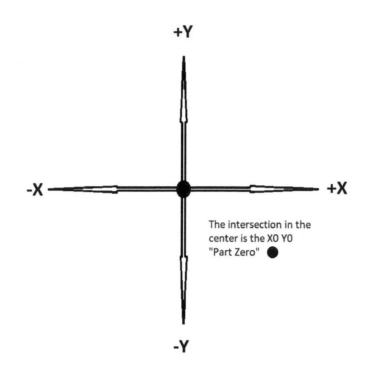

+Y

-X ———————— +X

The intersection in the
center is the X0 Y0
"Part Zero" ●

-Y

Setting an operating origin

As was discussed in chapter 3, a part origin zero must be set for X0 Y0. (Also Z0 for machines with a programmable Z axis.)

The part origin can be set anywhere on the work piece, or the fixture holding the work piece.

Typically, a corner of the work piece, the center of the work piece, or the center of a tooling ball will be used to set the part origin.

In most cases, if an operator is trained how to locate the corner of a work piece, and the center of a start hole. They will then have a good understanding of how to set a part origin anywhere within the machines working envelope.

Even though the Cartesian Coordinate System is the internal method used, the coordinate systems name on the machine, will go by many different names depending on the manufacture of the machine.

Examples of the different coordinate systems names are, Absolute, Relative, Working, User, Reference, G54, and others.

Some machine manufactures will use a combination of these different names, and offer different options for the programmers.

Whatever the case may be, one coordinate system origin zero must be selected for the program to work to.

It is common practice for an operator or programmer to work off of one coordinate system (Example G54), however, they may set other coordinate systems to the same zero. For emergency backups. (As a way to recover from a mishap)

CNC machines have different canned cycles built in that are used for locating and setting part origins. For example "Edge Finding", and "Center Finding".

Once a part origin is set, that will be the X0, Y0, and Z0 that the machine will work to when executing the operators selected program.

NOTES:

_____

_____

_____

_____

_____

_____

_____

_____

_____

_____

Example for one machines origin setting procedure (For a Wire EDM machine)

1. Press the wire thread button, on the hand pendent.

2. You can watch a simulated view of the wire threading by clicking on the **AWT** function, on the screen.

This is the AWT screen.

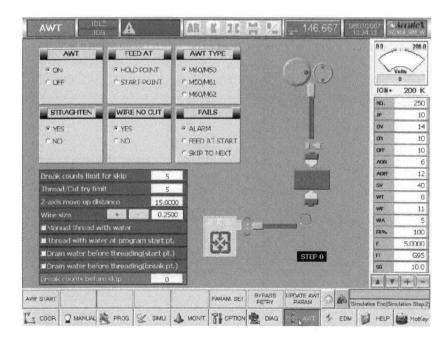

3. Now we will locate a king corner of the part, by locating two edges of the part.

4. Select the **COOR** function, on the screen. (Coordinates)

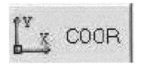

5. Using the movement buttons on the remote, position the wire near the **–X** edge of the part.

6. Press the EDGE button, on the hand pendent.

7. Press the X+ button, on the hand pendent. The wire feed should turn on, and the wire should move towards the part, and find the edge. Wait for the beep.

8. Select the **COOR** function, on the screen. (Coordinates)

9. Select the **ABSOLUTE** coordinate display, on the screen.

ABSOLUTE	▾		RELATIVE	▾		MACHINE	▾
X	0.0000		X	10.0000		X	285.7401
Y	5.0000		Y	0.0000		Y	39.2569
U	0.0000		U	0.0000		U	49.6005
V	0.0000		V	0.0000		V	50.2001
Z	146.6667		Z	146.6667		Z	146.6667
W	463.3933		W	463.3933		W	0.0000

WORK	▾		START COOR	▾		BREAK COOR	▾
X	41.1856		X	285.7401		X	285.7401
Y	-28.9356		Y	39.2569		Y	39.2569
U	0.7000		U	49.6005		U	49.6005
V	0.0000		V	50.2001		V	50.2001
Z	146.6667		Z	146.6667		Z	146.6667
W	1257.0423		W	0.0000		W	0.0000

10. Push the **NUM** lock button, on the hand pendent, and check for green light.

11. Click on the **ABC** function, on the screen, to bring up the dialog box.

12. This is the dialog box.

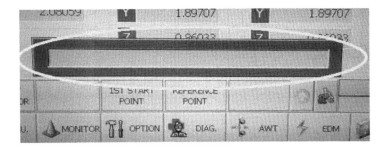

13. Input **X-.005** (½ of the wire diameter, of the wire being used), and press enter.

Note:

We just set the edge that we picked up, to be the **X0.0** location for the **Absolute Coordinate system**. We set the center of the wire to be -.005 away from the edge. We will now do the same for the **Work Coordinate System**.

14. Select the **Work** coordinate display, on the screen.

ABSOLUTE		RELATIVE		MACHINE	
X	0.0000	X	10.0000	X	285.7401
Y	5.0000	Y	0.0000	Y	39.2569
U	0.0000	U	0.0000	U	49.6005
V	0.0000	V	0.0000	V	50.2001
Z	46.6667	Z	146.6667	Z	146.6667
W	3.3933	W	463.3933	W	0.0000

WORK		START COOR		BREAK COOR	
X	41.1856	X	285.7401	X	285.7401
Y	-28.9356	Y	39.2569	Y	39.2569
U	0.7000	U	49.6005	U	49.6005
V	0.0000	V	50.2001	V	50.2001
Z	146.6667	Z	146.6667	Z	146.6667
W	1257.0423	W	0.0000	W	0.0000

15. Click on the **ABC** function, on the screen, to bring up the dialog box.

16. This is the dialog box.

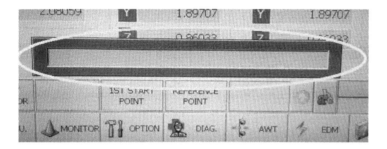

17. Input **X-.005** (½ of the wire diameter, of the wire being used), and press enter.

18. Click the ABC button to turn off the dialog box.

19. Repeat steps 29 to 42 for the Y axis, but you will now be edge finding the **+Y** edge of the part, instead of the **−X** edge of the part.

Note:

Now the **X0.0**, and the **Y0.0** should be set for both the **Absolute Coordinate System**, and the **Work Coordinate System**.

Note:

Now we will test to see if we set the origin correctly by following the next steps.

20. Move the X and Y axis away from the part, in the negative directions.

21. Click on the **MOVE BY ABS COOR** function, on the screen.

22. In the window that pops up, input **X0.0**, and **Y0.0**, but do not press enter until both values are typed in. Use the arrow buttons or the mouse to move from the **X AXIS TARGET BOX**, to the **Y AXIS TARGET BOX**.

Now we need to set the Z axis soft limit in a more accurate location, for better flushing.

23. Move the Z axis down to approximately .300 above the part for this training. When actually cutting, the upper flush cup should be just off the part surface by a few thousands of an inch.

Click on the soft limit function, on the screen, until it is updated, and red in color. (Red means soft limit active)

NOTES:

CENTER FINDING A START HOLE

Up until this point the only way of locating that has been discussed has been by using the EDGE FIND Function. However, it is very common to locate to a hole that has been put into the workpiece.

Example for one machine's center finding procedure.

1) Thread the wire through the hole.

2) Click on the Manual function on the screen.

3) Click on the Hole Center function on the screen.

4) Double check the parameters are set correct.

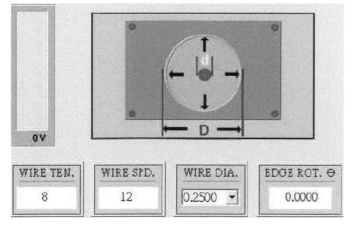

WIRE TEN.	WIRE SPD.	WIRE DIA.	EDGE ROT. ⊖
8	12	0.2500 ▾	0.0000

5) Press the Wire button on the pendent.

6) Check to make sure the Short Light, on the pendent, is off.

   SHORT

7) Press any direction key (+x, -x, +y, or −y) on the hand pendent.

8) Click on the coordinate function on the screen, and zero out the Absolute Coordinates origin, the same way that was done when using edge finding to locate the origins.

9) Repeat step 8 for the Work Coordinates origin.

Repeat the entire center finding procedure to check repeatability.

CHAPTER 5

THEORY OF CNC SKIM CUTTING

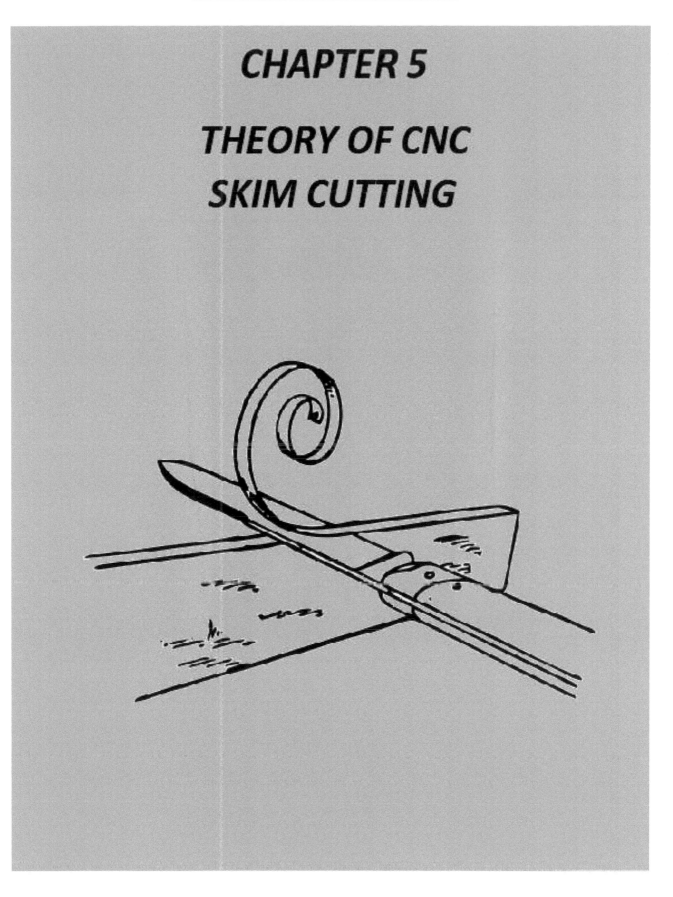

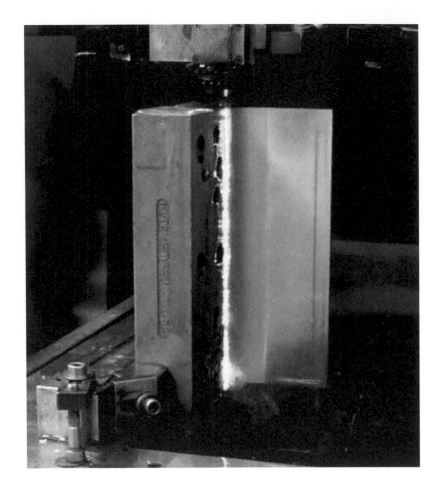

Chapter 5: Theory of CNC Skim Cutting

SKIM CUTTING

With any given power settings, there was a certain amount of Over Cut that naturally occurs, along with the surface finish that those settings produce.

If a fine finish is required, very low power settings are required. Trying to wire cut the entire shape with the low power settings required to produce the fine finish, would be an extremely slow and unproductive process.

Therefore a rough cut is first made to remove the bulk of the material quickly, and then a skim cut or skim cuts are made to smooth out the finish.

Skim cutting also improves the geometry of the cut, by straightening the walls, and sharpening the corners of the cut.

CNC Wire Machines have the ability to be programmed to **OFFSET** the wire path while traveling along the programmed path. Therefore a program can be set to rough cut with higher power settings leaving just enough stock to be removed later with skim cuts using low power settings.

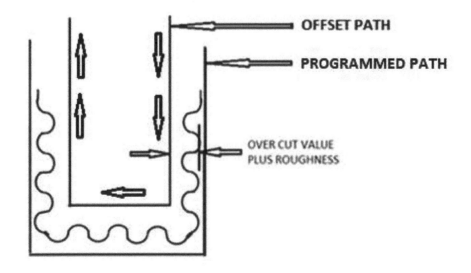

Imagine sawing a board in half, and then trying to smooth it out with a piece of fine sandpaper. This would be a very time consuming process.

In wood working this process is made much more efficient by sawing the board in half and then dividing the sanding process up into steps. Starting with rough sandpaper, and then stepping through many different grits of sandpaper. In a progression from rougher to smoother.

Skim cutting is using this same process. First we rough out the material, and then reduce the power settings in steps, while removing less stock with each step. Leaving the minimal amount of stock between each step. And leaving a smoother surface finish with each step.

In other words, the programmed offset value is reduced in steps along with the power settings being reduced.

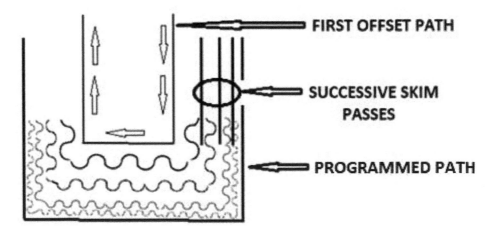

FIRST OFFSET PATH

SUCCESSIVE SKIM PASSES

PROGRAMMED PATH

ON BOARD TECHNOLOGY

With the addition of onboard technology, this process has become even more efficient with the use of cutting data that has been acquired through years of research and testing.

ON BOARD TECHNOLOGY is selected based on the size of the wire being used, the work material being cut, and the thickness of the work material being cut.

Once an **ON BOARD TECHNOLOGY** is chosen, the technology normally provides codes for the settings to be used with each skim cut, and the offsets that should be used with each skim cut.

SELECTING ON BOARD TECHNOLOGY

Here is an example of how technology is selected on one type of wire EDM machine, when **Skim Cutting**.

1) Click on the **EDM** function button, on the screen.

2) Find the **CONDITIONS** window on the screen, as shown below.

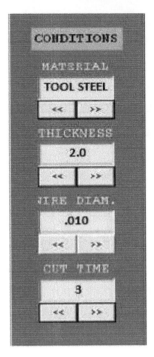

3) Select the **Material** that you want to cut. (Example = Tool Steel)

4) Select the closest **THICKNESS** that matches the thickness that you want to cut. (Example = 2.0 inches)

5) Select the **WIRE DIA** (Wire Diameter) of the wire that you are using. (Example = .010 inches)

6) Select the **CUT TIME** (Number of passes that you will make in your cut.) (Example = 1 rough + 2 skims = 3)

7) Click on the **EDM SEARCH** function button, on the screen.

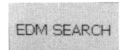

8) Click the **SEARCH** function, on the screen, to get the suggested settings for the cut selected.

The machine will now display the **Selected Technology**, as shown below.

NO.	1671	1672	1673		
IP	10	9	7		
OV	14	11	18		
ON	16	2	3		
OFF	10	4	8		
AON	11	2	3		
AOFF	10	4	8		
SV	23	37	42		
WT	12	12	15		
WF	12	14	12		
WA	8	1	1		
FR%	100	100	100		
F	3.5000	13.0000	20.0000		
SG	4.2	18.0	23.0		
OFFSET	.0086	.0056	.0052		

9) Write down the three suggested technology numbers, and the associated offset values to be used with them. These numbers will be put onto the program when it is written.

    A) Technology Number 1671, and Offset Value .0086 inches
    B) Technology Number 1672, and Offset Value .0056 inches
    C) Technology Number 1673, and Offset Value .0052 inches

Here is an example of how technology is selected on one type of wire EDM machine, when only **one pass** is being run.

1) Click on the **EDM** function button, on the screen.

2) Find the **CONDITIONS** window on the screen, as shown below.

3) Select the **Material** that you want to cut. (Example = Aluminum)

4) Select the closest **THICKNESS** that matches the thickness that you want to cut. (Example = 1.967 inches)

5) Select the **WIRE DIA** (Wire Diameter) of the wire that you are using. (Example = .010 inches)

6) Select the **CUT TIME** (Number of passes that you will make in your cut.) (Example = 1)

7) Click on the **EDM SEARCH** function button, on the screen.

8) Click the **SEARCH** function, on the screen, to get the suggested settings for the cut selected.

The machine will now display the **Selected Technology**, as shown below.

NO.	3671				
IP	10				
OV	11				
ON	11				
OFF	6				
AON	8				
AOFF	6				
SV	21				
WT	12				
WF	7				
WA	8				
FR%	100				
F	335				
SG	7				
OFFSET	.00795				

9) Write down the suggested technology number, and the associated offset value to be used with it. These numbers will be put onto the program when it is written.

A) Technology Number 3671, and Offset Value .00795

OFFSETTING THE WIRE

As we have discussed, every power setting (Technology) generates a certain amount of overcut, and any cut made with said power setting (Technology) will measure that amount larger. Therefore the wire should be offset by that amount.

Wire offset = ½ of the wire diameter + the overcut amount.

As we just discussed in the "skim cutting" and the "selecting technology" sections of this book, the programmed offset values will be reduced in steps, along with the power settings.

Wire offset = ½ of the wire diameter + the overcut amount + the amount of stock to leave for following skim cuts.

In the next section of this book, you will learn all of the Codes used to command the machine to preform different functions. However this is a good time to go into a detailed explanation of the **Offset Compensation Codes**. They are as follows.

G40 = Wire offset compensation off.

G41 = Wire offset compensation on, to the left of the programmed path.

G42 = Wire offset compensation on, to the right of the programmed path.

PROGRAMMED PATH

G40 = THE WIRE TRAVELS DIRECTLY
DOWN THE PROGRAMMED PATH

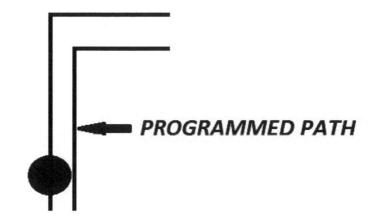

PROGRAMMED PATH

G41 = THE WIRE TRAVELS TO THE LEFT OF THE PROGRAMMED PATH.

PROGRAMMED PATH

G42 = THE WIRE TRAVELS TO THE RIGHT OF THE PROGRAMMED PATH.

NOTES:

CHAPTER 6

CODES

```
G90
G20
G95
G92 X0.0 Y0.0
G00 X0.0 Y0.325
M60
M85
S3671 D.00795
G41 G01 X0.0 Y.125
X.125 Y.125
X.125 Y-.125
X-.125 Y-.125
X-.125 Y.125
X0.0 Y.125
G40 X0.0 Y.325
M45
M02
```

Chapter 6: Codes

CODES

There are many CNC machines that use G & M Code programming.

Even though they should all use the same industry standard G & M Codes, there are some variances in the G & M Codes between machine manufactures, so you will need to consult your manufactures documentation.

G Codes are preparatory functions, and M Codes are miscellaneous functions. Both are sometimes followed by X-Y coordinates, or other variables.

Following is a list of some of the G CODES, definitions, and formats used by the manufacture of the machine used for the making of this book.

G CODES

CODE	DISCRIPTION	FORMAT
G20	INCH INPUT	G20
G21	METRIC INPUT	G21
G22	STORED STROKE LIMIT ON	G22_X_Y_I_J
G23	STORED STROKE LIMIT OFF	G23
G40	OFFSET COMPENSATION OFF	G40 X_Y_
G41	OFFSET COMPENSATION ON LEFT	G41 X_Y_D_
G42	OFFSET COMPENSATION ON RIGHT	G42 X_Y_D_
G50	TAPER OFF	G50
G51	TAPER ON LEFT	G51 X_Y_T_
G52	TAPER ON RIGHT	G52 X_Y_T_
G48	AUTOMATIC CORNER ON	G48
G49	AUTOMATIC CORNER OFF	G49
G60	WORK PIECE WITH EQUAL UP-DOWN CORNER	G60 X_Y_R_
G61	WORKPIECE WITH UNEQUAL UP-DOWN CORNER	G61 X_Y_R_
G90	ABSOLUTE COMMAND	G90
G91	INCREMENTAL COMMAND	G91
G92	PROGRAM START POINT SET	G92 X_Y_
G94	CONSTANT FEEDRATE	G94 F_
G95	SERVO FEEDRATE	G95
G00	RAPD TRAVERSE	G00 X_Y_U_V_
G01	LINEAR INTERPOLATION	G01 X_Y_U_V_

CODE	DISCRIPTION	FORMAT
G02	CLOCKWISE INTERPOLATION	G02 X_ Y_ I_ J_
G03	COUNTER-CLOCKWISE INTERPOLATION	G03 X_ Y_ I_ J_
G04	DWELL	G04 X_

Following is a list of some of the M CODES, definitions, and formats used by the manufacture of the machine used for the making of this book.

M CODES

CODE	DISCRIPTION	FORMAT
M00	PROGRAM STOP	M00
M01	OPTIONAL STOP	M01
M02	PROGRAM END	M02
M30	PROGRAM END AND REWIND	M30
M13	FEEDRATE OVERRIDE	M13 P_
M20	AUTOMATIC WIRE THREAD	M30
M21	AUTOMATIC WIRE CUT	M21
M60	AUTOMATIC WIRE THREAD	M60
M50	AUTOMATIC WIRE CUT	M50
M41	CUTTING POWER OFF	M41
M42	WIRE FEED OFF	M42
M43	FLUSH OFF	M43
M70	START POINT RETURN ALONG PROGRAM ROUTE	M70
M71	WIRE CUT AND START POINT RETURN DIRECT	M71
M81	CUTTING POWER ON	M81
M82	WIRE FEED ON	M82
M83	FLUSH ON	M83
M90	SERVO FEED (SAME AS G95)	M90
M91	CONSTANT FEED (SAME AS G94)	M91
M98	SUB PROGRAM CALL	M98 P_
M99	SUB PROGRAM RETURN	M99

CHAPTER 7
PROGRAMMING

```
G90
G20
G95
G92 X0.0 Y0.0
G00 X0.0 Y0.325
M60
M85
S3671 D.00795
G41 G01 X0.0 Y.125
X.125 Y.125
X.125 Y-.125
X-.125 Y-.125
X-.125 Y.125
X0.0 Y.125
G40 X0.0 Y.325
M45
M02
```

Chapter 7: Programming

PROGRAMMING

There are multiple ways to input a program into a Wire EDM Machine. A program can we written at the machine, written on a p.c. as a text document, or written using a Cad Cam system.

MANUAL DATA INPUT (MDI)

Manual Data Input is when a **G CODE / M CODE** program is entered, or edited, directly on the machines control panel.

EXAMPLE 1

For an example let's say that we had our workpiece origin (X0 Y0) set .100 from the edge of a workpiece, and that we want to cut into the workpiece .100, and then cut out a .250 square.

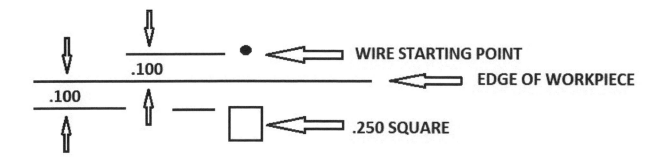

DEFINING POINTS

The points first need to be defined, so that a point to point program can be written.

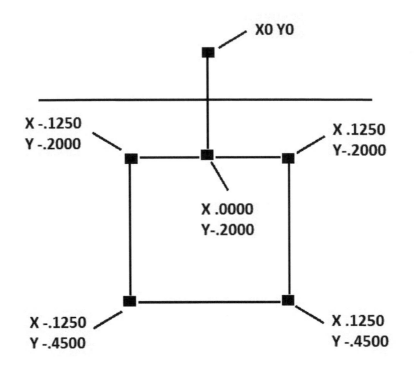

NOTE

We will say that for this example, the workpiece material is a 2 inch thick piece of Aluminum being cut with one cut, using .010 diameter wire. Therefore we can use the technology example from chapter 5 of this book.

Technology number = 3671
Wire offset value = .00795

EXAMPLE 1 PROGRAM WITH EXPLANATIONS

G90	(ABSOLUTE MODE ON)
G20	(INCH MODE ON)
G95	(SERVO CONTROLED FEEDRATE MODE ON)
G92 X 0.0000 Y 0.0000	(PROGRAM START POINT SET)
M60	(AUTOMATIC WIRE THREAD)
M85	(TANK FILL)
S3671 D.00795	(TECHNOLOGY AND WIRE OFFSET)
G41 G01 X 0.0000 Y -0.2000	(WIRE OFFSET LEFT, CUT TO FIRST POSITION)
X 0.1250 Y -0.2000	(CUT TO NEXT LOCATION)
X 0.1250 Y 0-.4500	(CUT TO NEXT LOCATION)
X -0.1250 Y -0.4500	(CUT TO NEXT LOCATION)
X -0.1250 Y -0.2000	(CUT TO NEXT LOCATION)
X 0.0000 Y -0.2000	(CUT TO NEXT LOCATION)
G40 X 0.0000 Y 0.0000	(WIRE OFFSET OFF, CUT TO LAST POSITION)
M45	(TANK DRAIN)
M02	(PROGRAM END)

PROGRAM AS ENTERED INTO THE MACHINE

G90
G20
G95
G92 X 0.0000 Y 0.0000
M60
M85
S3671 D.00795
G41 G01 X 0.0000 Y -0.2000
X 0.1250 Y -0.2000
X 0.1250 Y 0-.4500
X -0.1250 Y -0.4500
X -0.1250 Y -0.2000
X 0.0000 Y -0.2000
G40 X 0.0000 Y 0.0000
M45
M02

Example of one machines procedure for starting a new program.

1) Click on the "Program" function on the screen.

2) Click on the "Open" function on the screen.

3) Select the file called "New Program" and click on the "Open" function on the screen.

	Name	Size	Modified
⊟ MY MACHINE	0001	331	2006-03-04 14:27:00
HARD DISK	002.NC	272	2006-11-23 21:35:28
USBDISK	**NEW PROGRAM**		
	0421.NC	3,464	2006-04-21 11:14:52
	06-01.NC	202	2006-11-08 15:39:12
	06-02.NC	388	2006-11-08 15:40:22
	06-03.NC	529	2006-11-08 15:39:28
	11061C~1.NC	9,680	2005-10-17 16:27:26
	123456 89012.nc	341	2006-09-14 11:37:48
	12345678901.nc	341	2006-09-14 11:37:48
	3710.NC	2,330	2007-06-11 09:09:18
	45-17_.NC	411,583	2004-06-29 08:15:14
	45-22_.NC	414,762	2006-03-07 16:08:06
	48247	756	2006-06-14 17:06:08
	6-1.NC	230	2007-03-13 14:32:14
	6-2.NC	434	2007-03-13 14:33:00
	6-3.NC	584	2007-03-13 14:35:24
	6969	2,916	2006-06-14 17:06:14
	6side-1cut.NC	310	2006-11-24 09:49:06
	6side-2cut.NC	521	2006-11-24 09:49:42

FILENAME

OPEN   CANCEL

4) Click on the "Save file as" function on the screen.

5) Save the file under a new name. Possibly a job number.

6) Click on the "Open" function on the screen.

7) Select the file that you named, and click on the "Open" function on the screen.

8) Check for the correct file name to appear in the lower left corner of the screen.

9) Edit the program to read what you want. Then click on the "Save" function on the screen.

SAVE

TESTING A PROGRAM FOR ERRORS.

1) Click on the "Simulate" function in the screen.

2) Click on the "Load to online" function on the screen.

3) Click on the "Copy all data" function on the screen.

NOTES

The control will automatically go to "Monitor" mode, check the program for syntax errors, and draw a picture of the programs path.

If you click the "Show/Hide" function, you will see the drawing, and the program.

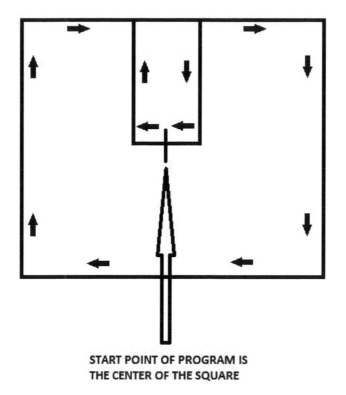

**START POINT OF PROGRAM IS
THE CENTER OF THE SQUARE**

EXAMPLE FOR 1 PASS ONLY

G90	(ABSOLUTE MODE ON) (G90 MODAL)
G20	(INCH MODE ON) (G20 MODAL)
G95	(SERVO CONTROLED FEEDRATE MODE ON) (G95 MODAL)
G92 X0.0 Y0.0	(PROGRAM START POINT SET)
M60	(AUTO WIRE THREAD)
M85	(TANK FILL)
S3671 D.00795	(TECHNOLOGY AND WIRE OFFSET)
G42 G01 X-0.02 Y0.0	(WIRE OFFSET RIGHT, CUT TO FIRST POSITION) (G42 AND G01 MODAL)
X-.02 Y0.25	(CUT TO NEXT POSITION)
X0.25 Y0.25	(CUT TO NEXT POSITION)
X0.25 Y-0.25	(CUT TO NEXT POSITION)
X-0.25 Y-0.25	(CUT TO NEXT POSITION)
X-0.25 Y0.25	(CUT TO NEXT POSITION)
X.02 Y0.25	(CUT TO NEXT POSITION)
X.02 Y0.0	(CUT TO NEXT POSITION)
G40 X0.0 Y0.0	(WIRE OFFSET OFF, CUT TO LAST POSITION)
M45	(TANK DRAIN)
M02	(PROGRAM END)

EXAMPLE FOR SKIM CUTS

G90	(ABSOLUTE MODE ON) (G90 MODAL)
G20	(INCH MODE ON) (G20 MODAL)
G95	(SERVO CONTROLED FEEDRATE MODE ON) (G95 MODAL)
G92 X0.0 Y0.0	(PROGRAM START POINT SET)
M60	(AUTO WIRE THREAD)
M85	(TANK FILL)
	(FIRST PASS)
S3671 D.00996	(TECHNOLOGY AND WIRE OFFSET)
G42 G01 X-0.02 Y0.0	(WIRE OFFSET RIGHT, CUT TO FIRST POSITION) (G42 AND G01 MODAL)
X-.02 Y0.25	(CUT TO NEXT POSITION)
X0.25 Y0.25	(CUT TO NEXT POSITION)
X0.25 Y-0.25	(CUT TO NEXT POSITION)
X-0.25 Y-0.25	(CUT TO NEXT POSITION)
X-0.25 Y0.25	(CUT TO NEXT POSITION)
X.02 Y0.25	(CUT TO NEXT POSITION)
X.02 Y0.0	(CUT TO NEXT POSITION)
G40 X0.0 Y0.0	(WIRE OFFSET OFF, CUT TO LAST POSITION)
	(SECOND PASS)
S3672 D.00602	
G42 G01 X-0.02 Y0.0	
X-.02 Y0.25	
X0.25 Y0.25	
X0.25 Y-0.25	
X-0.25 Y-0.25	
X-0.25 Y0.25	
X.02 Y0.25	
X.02 Y0.0	
G40 X0.0 Y0.0	
	(THIRD PASS)
S3673 D.00524	
G42 G01 X-0.02 Y0.0	
X-.05 Y0.25	
X0.25 Y0.25	
X0.25 Y-0.25	
X-0.25 Y-0.25	
X-0.25 Y0.25	
X.05 Y0.25	
X.05 Y0.0	
G40 X0.0 Y0.0	
M45	(TANK DRAIN)
M02	(PROGRAM END)

EXERCISE

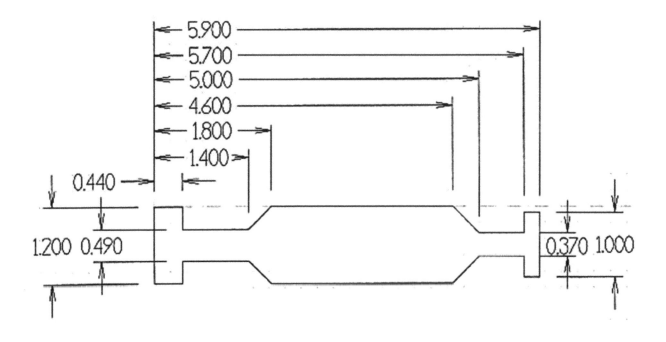

NOTES:

CHAPTER 8
RUNNING
THE
PROGRAM

Chapter 8: Running the Program

Running the program is done in steps.
1) Load the program.
2) Simulate the program on the screen, and check for illegal input errors.
3) Test the program via a dry run, and checking for problems.
4) Set the flushing and run the program.

Example of one machines procedure for loading the program.

1) Click on the "Program" function on the screen.

2) Click on the "Open" function on the screen.

3) Click on the program that you want to run and click on "Open".

Name	Size	Modified
MY MACHINE		
HARD DISK		
USBDISK		
0001	331	2006-03-04 14:27:00
002.NC	272	2006-11-23 21:35:28
YOUR PROGRAM		
0421.NC	3,464	2006-04-21 11:14:52
06-01.NC	202	2006-11-08 15:39:12
06-02.NC	388	2006-11-08 15:40:22
06-03.NC	529	2006-11-08 15:39:28
1106lC~1.NC	9,680	2005-10-17 16:27:26
123456 89012.nc	341	2006-09-14 11:37:48
12345678901.nc	341	2006-09-14 11:37:48
3710.NC	2,330	2007-06-11 09:09:18
45-17_.NC	411,583	2004-06-29 08:15:14
45-22_.NC	414,762	2006-03-07 16:08:06
48247	756	2006-06-14 17:06:08
6-1.NC	230	2007-03-13 14:32:14
6-2.NC	434	2007-03-13 14:33:00
6-3.NC	584	2007-03-13 14:35:24
6969	2,916	2006-06-14 17:06:14
6side-1cut.NC	310	2006-11-24 09:49:06
6side-2cut.NC	521	2006-11-24 09:49:42

FILENAME   OPEN   CANCEL

4) Click on the "Simulate" function on the screen.

5) Click on the "Load to Online" function on the screen.

6) Click on the "Copy all Data" function on the screen.

Note:

If no illegal input errors have been made the control will automatically go into the "Monitor Screen" and draw the program path that was selected.

DRY RUNNING A PROGRAM

Dry running a program means to run the program through all of the programs motions, except for threading the wire, turning on the pumps, or turning on the generator for cutting. Dry running can help eliminate many costly mistakes. For examples, dry running can show:

A) If the program will fit within the machines working envelope. (Axis Limits)
B) If the programmed path will clear all obstacles, such as clamps and tooling.
C) If a dimension was entered wrong, in some cases.
D) If a programmed stop was missed.
E) And more….

Example of one machines procedure for Dry Running the program.

1) Make sure the wire is cut and that the machine is sitting at the programs start position. (Normally the origin X zero, and Y zero)

2) Locate the Hand Pendent.

3) On the hand pendent, select the "Auto" mode

4) On the hand pendent, select the "Dry Run" mode.

5) On the screen, select the "Show/Hide" function until **both** the **program**, and **the part** are displayed on the screen.

```
(D:\002.WRK)
%
G91
N1
M20
G92X-29.548Y31.639
G41H01E1
G01X-0.754Y-3.928
G02X0.681Y-0.151I-2.358J-12.276
G02X0.144Y-0.246I-0.049J-0.194
G01X-0.673Y-2.511
G02X-0.241Y-0.143I-0.193I0.051
G03X-1.267Y0.222I-2.269J-9.225
G03X-0.22Y-0.182I-0.021I-0.199
G01X-0.135Y-1.595
G03X0.177Y-0.215I0.199I-0.016
G02X0.031Y-0.004I-0.824J-7.455
G03X0.221Y0.171I0.023J0.199
G01X0.084Y0.594
G02X0.231Y0.17I0.198J-0.028
G02X0.066Y-0.012I-1.391J-8.386
G02X0.162Y-0.236I-0.034J-0.197
G01X-0.117Y-0.588
G03X0.152Y-0.234I0.196J-0.039
G02X0.03Y-0.007I-1.654J-7.316
```

6) Prepare to watch the program dry run, and to prepare to press the program Stop button on the hand pendent (or if that fails the E-Stop), if anything goes wrong. For example if one of the heads is about to crash into something.

7) To Dry Run the program, press the Cycle Start button, on the hand pendent.

8) After the program has finished running, turn off the Dry Run function, on the hand pendent.

9) Put the machine back in manual mode by turning on the Jog function, on the hand pendent.

START POINT RETURN

If the program does not return the machine to the original start position, if the machine is E-stopped in the middle of the program, or if the program is reset in the middle of a program, the machine must be returned to the start position manually. This can be done by following these steps.

1) Click on the "Hotkey" function, on the screen.

2) Click the "Reset" function, in the window that pops up, on the screen.

3) Select the "Start Point Return" function, on the hand pendent.

4) Verify that the machine has returned to the start point by checking the coordinate readouts, on the screen.

BREAK POINT RETURN

If the program is stopped in the middle, but no axis is manually moved, the program can just be started back running. But, if a program is stopped in the middle, and one or more axis are moved manually, then the machine axis must be returned to the original stopped position before starting the program back running. This can be done by following these steps.

1) Select the "Break Point Return" function on the hand pendent.

2) Verify that "Return OK" is displayed on the screen, and that all axis have returned to the location of the interruption.

3) If all axis have returned to the location prior to the interruption, then select the Cycle Start function on the remote control.

SETTING THE FLUSHING

There are two different conditions for setting the flushing on a Wire EDM machine. Condition one is a single cut, or a first pass cut. The second condition is for a skim cut, or a cut that takes place after the slug has been removed.

SETTING THE FLUSH FOR A SINGLE CUT OR A FIRST PASS CUT.

1) If the wire is not already cut, select the "Automatic Wire Cut" function, on the hand pendent.

2) Position the machine so that the upper head is over a flat area of the part.

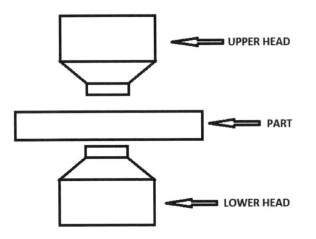

3) Unlock the Z soft limit by selecting it on the screen (Red = Locked).

4) Jog (Lower) the Z axis until the upper head is about .05 above the part.

5) Select the "Fill Tank" function, on the hand pendent.

6) Once the water level in the tank reaches the upper head, select the "Flush" function, on the hand pendent.

7) Select the X10 (.001) Step function, on the hand pendent.

8) Select the "Incremental Jog" function, on the hand pendent.

9) Increment the Z axis down until the top guide pressure matches the lower guide pressure, and then lock the Z axis Soft Limit.

SETTING THE FLUSH FOR A SKIM CUT

When skim cutting is being done, the slug has normally been removed and the cut is open. High pressure flushing is not necessary, and a low pressure should be used. The flushing should be adjusted for what we will refer to as the umbrella effect. This is where the upper head pressure and the lower head pressure is adjusted to create an umbrella like shape in the middle of the work piece.

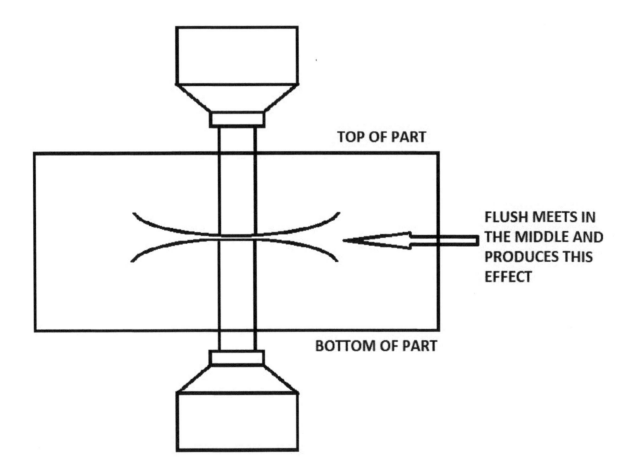

TOP OF PART

FLUSH MEETS IN THE MIDDLE AND PRODUCES THIS EFFECT

BOTTOM OF PART

CHAPTER 9
TAPER CUTTING

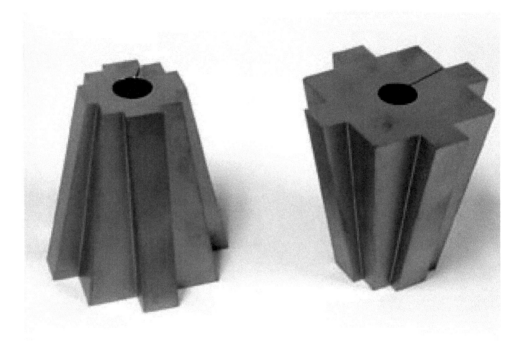

Chapter 9: Taper Cutting

G Codes

The G Codes that are used for cutting taper are G50 (Taper off), G51 (Taper on left), and G52 (Taper on right). The variable **T** is used to define the taper angle. Below is the same "Example one pass (cut) only" square program from chapter 7, with the correct taper commands added.

G90
G20
G95
G92 X0.0 Y0.0
M60
M85
S3671 D.00795
G42 **G52** G01 X-0.02 Y0.0 **T3.0**   (Taper on right, angle equals 3.0 degrees)
X-.02 Y0.25
X0.25 Y0.25
X0.25 Y-0.25
X-0.25 Y-0.25
X-0.25 Y0.25
X.02 Y0.25
X.02 Y0.0
G40 **G50** X0.0 Y0.0   (Taper off)
M45
M02

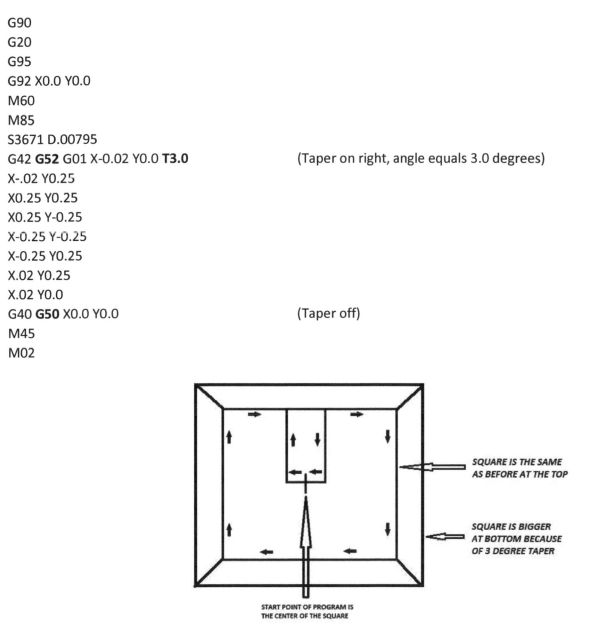

SQUARE IS THE SAME
AS BEFORE AT THE TOP

SQUARE IS BIGGER
AT BOTTOM BECAUSE
OF 3 DEGREE TAPER

START POINT OF PROGRAM IS
THE CENTER OF THE SQUARE

TAPER SETTINGS

When cutting taper, there are parameters on the Wire EDM machines that also need to be set properly, in addition to adding the G Codes to the program. The names of these parameters may vary from one manufacture to another, but the values entered are normally the same. There is normally two parameters that need to be set. The programmed plane, and the center plane of the taper. Following are four examples of how these values are calculated.

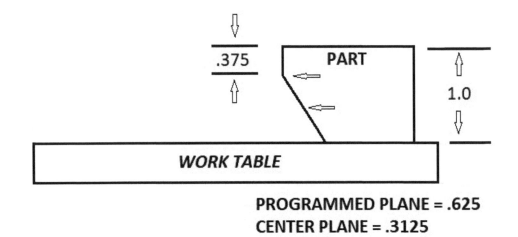

PROGRAMMED PLANE = .625
CENTER PLANE = .3125

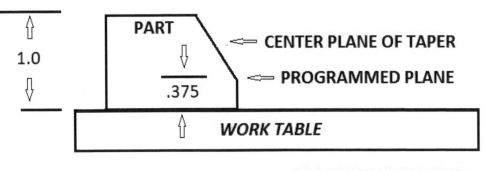

PROGRAMMED PLANE = .375
CENTER PLANE = .6875

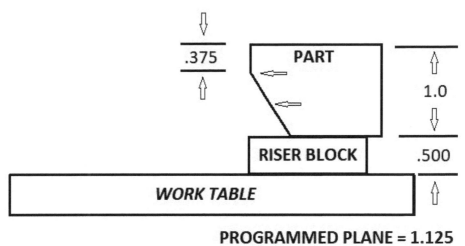

PROGRAMMED PLANE = 1.125
CENTER PLANE = .8125

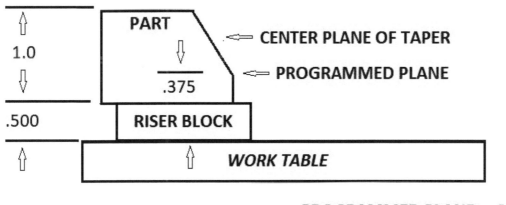

PROGRAMMED PLANE = .875
CENTER PLANE = 1.1875

Programmed plane = The plane that the X, Y, and Z axis were programmed to.

Center Plane = The center of the taper thickness.

The examples shown are for 2-Axis programming, with land, lead in, and relief angles, but the same holds true for 4-Axis programming.

Example of one machines taper registers

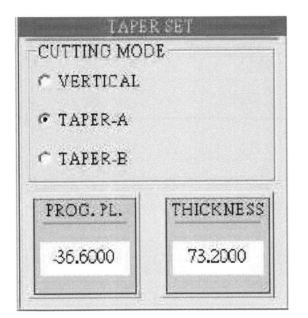

NOTES:

_____

_____

_____

_____

_____

_____

_____

_____

_____

_____

_____

_____

_____

CHAPTER 10
OFFLINE PROGRAMMING
AND FILE TRANSFER

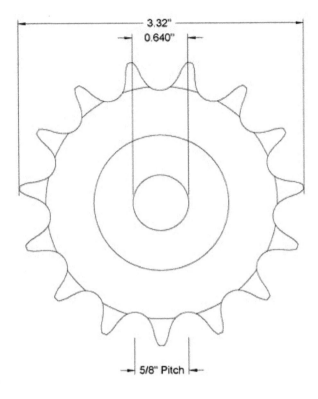

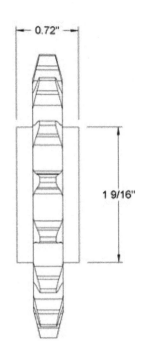

Chapter 10: Offline Programming and File Transfer

Programming

As discussed in chapter 7 of this book, Manual Data Input (MDI) is programming directly at the machines control panel, and entering a program that uses G Codes, and M Codes.

Offline programming can refer to programming at a P.C. using a word processor software, or programming at a P.C. using Cad Cam software.

It is necessary to learn MDI programming because it is very common to have to make adjustments to the program at the machine.

It is also necessary to learn MDI G Code/ M Code programming because it is very common for Cad Cam system's post processor to **not** be made specifically for your Wire EDM machine.

Different ways of transferring files to the EDM machine

There are different ways of transmitting files to the EDM machine.

A) Via a USB Drive
B) Via a RS232 Cable
C) Via a Ethernet Cable

We will be using a USB drive. Also called a "jump drive", "Flash Drive", "Thumb Drive", or "Memory Stick".

Format

Before files can be transferred from an offline source, the machines required format must be know.

For example common file extensions in the EDM world are:

A) .NC
B) .TXT
C) .ISO

The machine that is being used for this book requires files names with 8 characters or less, and no extension.

NOTES: _____

_____

_____

_____

_____

_____

_____

_____

_____

_____

_____

_____

_____

_____

Example steps for transferring a file from one type of Cad Cam system, to one type of Wire EDM machine.

A) Draw the part geometry in the Cad Cam software.

B) Define the tool path in the Cad Cam software.

C) Run the Cad Cam's post processor, and save the outputted file to the P.C.'s desk top.

D) Open the saved file with a word processor software, such as Microsoft Word.

E) Edit the file so that the program contains exactly what information your EDM machine needs, and resave the file.

F) Rename the file if necessary for the correct extension, and characters.

G) Save the file to a USB drive (Memory Stick).

H) Insert the USB drive (Memory Stick) into the USB port of the Wire EDM machine.

I) Select the **PROGRAM** function button, on the screen.

J) Select the **FILE MANAGEMENT** function button, on the screen.

K) Select **USB**.

L) Select the file you want to transfer.

M) Select **COPY**.

N) Select **HARD DRIVE**.

O) Select **PASTE**.

P) Select **CANCEL**.

Q) Select **OPEN**.

R) Select the file you want to open.

S) Select **OPEN**.

T) Select **SIMULATE**.

U) Select **LOAD TO ONLINE**.

V) Select **COPY ALL DATA**.

The machine will now check the program for input errors, and draw a picture of the program path.

EXAMPLE: Output from post processor may look like this.

```
%
o0001 (JOHNDOEPROGRAM)
(DATE-DD-MM-YY-23-04-15 TIME-HH:MM 19:50)
(MCX FILE-E:\CADCAM-WIRE\JOHNDOEFILE.NC)
N100 G0 G20 G90
N110 G92 X 0.0000 Y 0.0000 I0.0 J 0.0
N120 G0 X0 Y0
N130 M60
N140 M35 M81
N160 G41 G1 X 0.0000 Y -0.2000
N170 X 0.1250 Y -0.2000
N180 X 0.1250 Y 0-.4500
N190 X -0.1250 Y -0.4500
N200 X -0.1250 Y -0.2000
N210 X 0.0000 Y -0.2000
N220 G40 X 0.0000 Y 0.0000
N230 M50
N240 M30
%
```

EXAMPLE: Same program after editing for your machine.

```
G90 G20 G95
G92 X 0.0000 Y 0.0000
M60
M85
S3671 D.00795
G41 G01 X 0.0000 Y -0.2000
X 0.1250 Y -0.2000
X 0.1250 Y 0-.4500
X -0.1250 Y -0.4500
X -0.1250 Y -0.2000
X 0.0000 Y -0.2000
G40 X 0.0000 Y 0.0000
M45
M02
```